ABOUT THE PARABLES

Jesus taught people what God is like and how God plans for us to live. He taught in many ways—by what he did and by what he said. Often he taught by telling stories. The followers of Jesus remembered these stories and wrote them down. They are now in the Bible.

Some of the stories explain how God loves people and forgives them. Some stories show how God expects people to love God and love one another. Some show how important each one of us is to God. Other stories tell how God wants us to live.

Many of these stories are called parables. Jesus taught in parables because they helped people to remember. He used everyday events to tell what people who are faithful to God should do.

Some of the parables of Jesus are retold in this book. They are retold in words and thoughts commonly used today, many, many years after they were first told by Jesus.

A.K.

STORIES JESUS TOLD

By Anita Klever

Illustrated by Jo Polseno

 RAND M^cNALLY & COMPANY

To my husband

JERRY

CONTENTS

The Story of the Lost Sheep

(Luke 15:3–7)

THERE WAS once a shepherd who had a large flock of sheep, one hundred of them. He walked many miles with his sheep each day to find grass and water.

One day the sheep wandered very far. It was dark by the time the shepherd brought them back home to the sheepfold. The sheepfold was made of stones piled into a wall which surrounded the sheep. It kept the animals safe from wild animals and robbers.

The shepherd drove his sheep through a small gate that led into the fold. As each one passed through the

9

gate, he counted, "One, two, three, four, . . . ninety-five, ninety-six, ninety-seven, ninety-eight, ninety-nine, . . . " He looked around for another sheep. There were one hundred in his flock. Where was the last sheep?

He rolled a large stone in front of the gate of the sheepfold and walked around the wall, calling in a low voice as he went. The sound of his voice would be familiar to the missing lamb. The shepherd hoped it would bring him running. But he could not find the stray lamb.

There were other sheepfolds nearby. The shepherd walked to one and asked the herder, "Have you seen a stray lamb?"

This man was seated near his fire eating his supper. "I have been here since before sundown and have seen nothing," he said.

The shepherd walked to the next fold. This man was mending the top of the wall of his fold. "I have lost one of my lambs. Have you seen a stray lamb?"

"I have seen nothing but my own flock. But I will look for your lamb and tell you if I find him."

The shepherd asked several other men in nearby folds, but none of them had seen the stray lamb.

He returned to his own fold and climbed to the top of the rock wall. In the moonlight, he again counted the sheep in the fold, "One, two, three, four, . . . ninety-seven, ninety-eight, ninety-nine. I was right the first time. One lamb is missing."

Looking to make sure that the rock in front of the sheepfold gate was solidly in place, the herder began to go back over his steps of the day. He walked and walked. He knew these pastures and their hills very well or he, too, might have become lost. The moon was hidden by clouds. It began to rain. He wished for a cup of warm milk and the covering of his blanket.

The shepherd looked behind big rocks and in thorny bushes. He was very tired. "Soon it will be daylight," he thought, "and I must water the other sheep in my flock."

Just as he was turning back he heard the faint bleat-
ing of a lamb, a soft "Baa . . . baa . . . baa . . . baa."
The shepherd forgot that he was tired and hungry.
Quickly he followed the sound. He found the lamb
caught in some thorny bushes. The shepherd reached
down. He spoke quietly. "Now there, don't struggle so
much. I'll cut you loose. You'll be safe in a minute."
The lamb heard the voice he knew. He became quiet.

Soon he was free from the thorns. The shepherd lifted the frightened little creature into his arms and carried him back to the sheepfold.

When the shepherd reached his fold, the sun was just coming up. The other herders were awake and saw him return. "You found the little fellow, I see," said one. "Where did you find him?" asked another.

The shepherd said to his friends, "He was caught in a thorn bush. Come, share some of the morning milk with me. I am happy that I have found my lost lamb."

The Story of the Good Samaritan

(Luke 10:29–37)

ONCE THERE was a man who was traveling from Jerusalem to Jericho. The road on which he was walking was dangerous. There were hills to climb, and many robbers hid in the caves along this road.

As the man came along, a group of robbers saw him. He was all alone and there was no one else nearby. The robbers jumped upon the man and beat him. When the man was unconscious they took most of his clothes and all his money, and left him by the road almost dead.

It was several hours before anyone came along the

road. Then a priest came by. He was hurrying, hoping to be in Jericho before evening. He did not like walking along this road. As he came around the curve in the road, he was frightened to see the body of a man lying there. Instead of stopping to see if he could help the man, the priest crossed quickly to the other side of the road and hurried on toward Jericho.

It was not long until another man, a Levite who sang in the temple, passed by. When he saw the beaten body of the man, he looked around sharply to see if there were any robbers still hiding nearby. Then he picked up a large stick beside the road and began to walk faster. He looked back to make sure no one was following.

The man lying beside the road did not move.

Then another person came along the road. He was a stranger in the country, a man from Samaria. He had heard stories of the dangers along this road. He, too, wanted to be safely in Jericho by evening. In addition, he had a special worry. He knew that in this country people were unfriendly toward Samaritans. He was not allowed to go many places, just because he was a Samaritan.

But when the Samaritan saw the man lying beside the road, he stopped. He could see that the man was bleeding, had dirt in his wounds, and had several broken bones. The Samaritan went to the mule on which he was carrying his things and took some of his own valuable medicine—oil and wine—to clean and treat the wounds. Taking pieces of clean cloth from his own clothing, he bandaged the man's cuts and bound his broken bones as best he could.

When he was finished, he repacked his mule and made room for the injured man. Gently the Samaritan lifted the man and put him on the donkey. Walking carefully and slowly, the Samaritan followed the road until finally he came to an inn. He got a room for the man, carried him to his bed, and made him comfortable for the night.

The next morning the Samaritan prepared to leave the hotel. He needed to hurry, as he had already lost a great deal of time. People were waiting to see him in Jericho. As he started to go, he handed the innkeeper some money. He said, "Take care of the man for me. I will pay you whatever you spend when I come through here on my return trip."

The Story of the Mustard Seed

(Matthew 13:31)

ONCE THERE was a farmer who was preparing to plant his fields. He plowed the ground. Then he raked the dirt until it was smooth. Now it was ready for planting.

When he had finished his other planting, he decided he would plant a mustard seed. He looked at the tiny seed and thought, "This surely is the smallest seed that I have ever seen. Can anything useful grow from such a small seed?"

He placed the tiny seed in the ground at the end of one row. He could hardly see the seed, because it was so small. He covered it quickly so birds would not eat it and the wind would not blow it away.

As the weeks passed, the sun shone on the seed. The rain gave it water. Soon it began to grow and a green shoot appeared above the ground. The little seed grew and grew. Before many weeks had passed the plant was the size of a small tree. It was large enough for the birds to sit on its limbs and build their nests in its branches.

The farmer was pleased. From the small seed had grown a tree.

The Story of the Talents

(Matthew 25:14–30)

ONCE A man who had lots of property and many people working for him decided to take a trip. He would be gone a long time. He decided to entrust some money to three of his employees to use while he was away. He decided to divide the money according to the experience of each man. In this way, each one would have a fair chance.

He said to the first man, "I am going on a trip and will be gone a long time. I am going to give you five talents [*about $5,000*]. You may invest this money any way you wish. When I return I shall see how well you have done."

To the second man he said, "I am leaving on a trip. Before I go, I am giving you two talents [*about $2,000*]. Use these talents wisely."

At last the third man was called. "I am going on a long journey. But before I go, I want to give you one talent [*about $1,000*] to use while I am gone."

The three employees wondered how they should use the money given to them. Each saw many good and many foolish ways to use his money.

The first man decided to trade his money for a piece of land. Later, he was able to sell this land for

twice as many talents as the rich man had given him.

The second man looked about carefully. He decided to trade his money for sheep. Their value increased. When he sold them, he had four talents instead of two.

But the third man was afraid that he might make a mistake. So instead of using his money, he went out in his yard, dug a hole, and buried his talent. He said to himself, "I am very wise. When the rich man returns, he will be pleased that I have not lost his talent."

After many months, the rich man returned from his trip. He had not been home long, when he thought, "I wonder how my three employees have used the talents which I gave them?"

The first man was very happy to see his employer, and said, "Did you have a nice trip, sir?"

"Yes, I did," the rich man said. "But it is good to be home. I am interested to learn how you used the five talents which I gave you."

"I was able to find a piece of land which I bought for five talents. Some time after I bought it, another

man bought it from me. Here are the five talents which you gave me, plus five more."

The rich man was pleased. "Very well done," he said. "You have been a good and faithful employee. You have been wise with the talents which I gave you. I will make you supervisor over much of my business."

The rich man called in the second man. "How have you been?" he asked.

"Fine, sir. I want to return the two talents which you gave me, plus two more which I was able to earn."

The rich man was pleased. "You are a careful worker and have returned to me more than I gave you. Because

you have been faithful with a little, I will place you in charge of a whole department of my business."

The rich man called the third employee to his office. "Did you have a nice journey?" the man asked.

"Yes, very nice, thank you. But I am interested in you. What have you done with the talent which I gave you?"

"I have been very careful with it, and here it is." The man gave the talent to the rich man.

"Is this all that you have?" asked the rich man.

"You gave me only one talent, sir," the employee replied.

"But what did you do with the talent while I was away?"

"I put it in a box and buried it in my yard so that no one could steal it from me. I wanted to keep the talent safe for you when you returned."

"Did you try to use the talent?"

"I looked at some things, but soon decided that the safest way to keep the talent was to hide it."

The rich man said, "You did not even try to use the talent which I gave you. If you cannot use one talent wisely, I cannot trust you with more. I am going to give your talent to the other men who know how to use what is given to them."

The Story of the Unmerciful Servant

(Matthew 18:23–35)

ONCE THERE was a King who was generous and often lent his employees money. One day the King was looking over his accounts. He discovered that some of these people were late in paying back the money. It was time they paid him. He was surprised when he began checking the account of one of his most important employees. He asked the employee to come to see him.

The employee was very nervous when he appeared before the King.

The King said, "I have been looking over your

account. Do you know how much money you owe me?"

The employee answered, "It is a large amount, sir, several thousand talents."

"Yes, you owe ten thousand talents. It has been a long time since you began to borrow from me. You have continued to borrow from me month after month and have never paid back any of the money."

The employee began to make excuses. "It has been many months. But the bills for my family are larger. Food costs more money today. Our new house cost more than we had planned."

The King asked, "Can you pay me any money at all?"

The employee replied, "I do not have any money now. Perhaps in a few months I shall have some money. Then I will try to repay you."

The King looked at his employee sternly. He was annoyed. "But you promised to pay it back," he said. "If you do not repay the money which I have loaned

to you, I shall have to take your house and your land.
I shall arrange for your wife and children to have jobs,
working for a friend of mine. I shall also give you a harder
job, and the money which you earn will be given to me
until I have been paid back what you owe me."

Now the employee was frightened. He pleaded,
"Don't take my wife and children from me! Let me con-
tinue to work for you. Please trust me; I will pay back
all that I owe you. I will begin paying this very week."

The King felt sorry for his employee. He really did
not want to take his belongings or separate his family.

So he said, "Very well. I shall give you one more chance. Do not disappoint me this time."

The employee walked out of the King's house and down the street toward his home. As he walked, he began to think how he could repay the money he owed: "We shall have to cut down our buying. We shall not be able to build that addition on our home for a few years. But I do not want to give up our vacation."

Just then he saw one of his fellow workers coming toward him. He thought, "This fellow owes me one hundred denarii [*about $20*]. I loaned it to him several months ago and he hasn't paid me back. It is a small sum but it will help."

As the fellow came nearer he called a greeting, "How are you today?" The chief employee grabbed his friend roughly by the coat collar. "Hey, what about that one hundred denarii you owe me? When do I get my money?"

"I'll give it to you by the first of next month. I won't have the money until I receive my pay."

"Do you think I am made of money?" shouted the chief employee. "You are at least a month late."

"Give me time. I will pay you," the friend begged.

But the chief employee refused. He had his fellow worker put into jail because he could not pay his debt.

All the other employees of the King were angry when they heard what had happened. One of them went to the King and asked, "Is it possible for me to borrow one hundred denarii of my pay in advance?"

"Why do you need to do this?" the King asked.

"One of the men who works with me has been thrown into jail for not repaying a loan. I want to repay it for him so he may be released from jail."

"Who would put a man into prison for being late in repaying a one hundred denarii loan?"

"One of your chief employees, sir."

When the King learned who it was, he was angry. He asked that his chief employee be brought to him at once.

He spoke sternly. "You ungrateful man! You have owed me money—a large sum—for several years and have not repaid any of it. When you asked for more time to repay me, I felt sorry for you. I did not have you thrown into jail, or sent to another job, or have any of your wages withheld. You were given still another chance. Yet, you had just left my office when you met your own fellow worker who owed you a small debt. He was only a few weeks late in repaying you. Yet you had him arrested and thrown into prison. When I forgave you for not paying a large debt, could you not forgive your fellow worker for not repaying a small debt?" And the King took away his chief employee's possessions and put him in jail.

The Story of the Sower

(Matthew 13:3–9, 18–23)

A FARMER went to plant his fields. He had plowed the field well and had chosen good seed. The farmer did not have a machine to plant the seeds, so he did it himself. He walked through his fields scattering the seeds along the plowed rows.

As the seeds fell from the farmer's hand, some landed on the road that ran along the edge of the field. Other seeds fell on stones and low rock ledges. Some seeds fell in thorny bushes. But much of the seed was planted in the good dirt of the plowed field.

The rains came and gave the seeds water, and the sun shone and gave the seeds warmth. The seeds began to grow.

Those seeds that had landed on the road were eaten by birds soon after the farmer had scattered the seeds.

The seeds that had landed on the stones began to grow, but there was very little dirt on the stones. The seeds could not build deep roots needed to hold the water for the plant. When the sun grew hot, the new plants withered and died.

The seeds that fell among the thorny bushes began to grow. But the bushes were big and strong. They kept the little seeds from getting any sunlight, or moisture. Soon these little seedlings were choked by the thorns.

But the seeds that the farmer planted on good dirt grew. They had deep roots, plenty of moisture, and warm sunshine. They grew strong and healthy. Soon they had golden grain. Some of the plants brought forth thirty bushels per acre. Others yielded sixty bushels. Some plants even brought forth one hundred bushels.

Jesus said that we are like the soils in which the farmer planted the seed. Some do not let seeds grow. Some are too hard, some are too shallow, some are too full of weeds. But some are soils that help seeds grow strong and healthy.

The Story of the Prodigal Son

(Luke 15:11–32)

THERE WAS a man who had two sons. One day the younger son said, "Father, give me my share of what you own that will some day be mine."

So the father took his property—his land, money, and household goods—and divided it between his two sons. Not many days had passed when the younger son took his share of his father's money and went to live in a country far away.

The younger son found that spending money was easy. He could find so many things to buy! So many people said they wanted to be his friends! He was having a wonderful and exciting life. At home he never had money to spend like this because his father did not live this way.

But soon all the money was gone. Now his new friends left him alone. At this time, there was little food in that country, and jobs were hard to find. The young man no longer had money to pay the high prices for the food that was for sale.

Rather than starve, he went to work for one of the farmers. He was given the job of feeding the pigs. He was so hungry that he would have gladly eaten the food the pigs ate.

The young man began to think of his father. He thought, "How foolish I have been! How wrong."

He remembered the home he had left. "My father's hired men have plenty of bread to eat. Here I am, in a far country, dying of hunger!"

Finally the young man decided. "I will go to my father. I will say to him, 'Father, I have sinned against heaven and before you. I should no longer be called your son. Let me work as one of your hired men.' "

So the young man started toward his father's home. He had to walk the entire distance. It took many days for him to make the journey. He was hungry and tired.

When the young man was near his father's house, someone saw him coming and told his father. His father ran to meet his son and threw his arms around him and kissed him.

The son said, "Father, I have sinned against heaven and before you; I should not be called your son."

But before he could say any more of the words that he had practiced, his father called to a helper. "Bring out the best robe that we have and put it on him! Put a ring on his finger. Find shoes for his feet. Kill one of the fat calves and cook it. Let us eat and rejoice, for my son has returned. He was lost and is found." And the father was happy that his son had come home.

The older son, the son who had stayed home, had been working in the fields. As he returned home, he heard music and dancing. He called to one of the servants, "What is all this noise? Why are we having a party?"

The servant replied, "Your brother has come home. Your father has killed a calf and is having a fine dinner because your brother is home safe and sound."

The older brother was angry and would not go inside. Finally his father came out to him and begged him to come in and join them. The older son replied, "All of these years I have worked with you. I have never disobeyed your wishes. Have you ever given me a party? No. But when my brother returns after he has spent his money on foolish things, you order a fine dinner for him."

The father said to him, "My son, you are always with me. All that I have is yours. But shouldn't we be happy that your brother has returned? He lost himself with foolish ideas, and has now found himself again. He has come home! Let us be glad."

PRINTED IN U.S.A.